LAWNMAGEDDON

Written by **PAUL TOBIN**
Art by **RON CHAN**
Colors by **MATTHEW J. RAINWATER**
Letters by **STEVE DUTRO**
Cover by **RON CHAN**

DARK HORSE BOOKS

PLANTS VS. ZOMBIES

LAWNMAGEDDON

Publisher **MIKE RICHARDSO**
Editor **PHILIP R. SIMO**
Assistant Editor **EVERETT PATTERSO**
Designer **KAT LARSO**
Digital Production **CHRISTINA MCKENZI**

Special thanks to SHANA DOERR, AMY
HEVRON, A.J. RATHBUN, PHILIP SMITH,
BRENNAN TOWNLEY, JEREMY VANHOOZER,
and everyone at PopCap Games.

This volume collects *Plants vs. Zombies:
Lawnmageddon* #1–#6, originally serialized
by Dark Horse Digital.

Published by Dark Horse Books, a division of
Dark Horse Comics, Inc., 10956 SE Main Street,
Milwaukie, OR 97222
International Licensing: (503) 905-2377

To find a comics shop in your area, call the Comic
Shop Locator Service toll-free at 1-888-266-4226.

Scholastic edition: January 2014
ISBN 978-1-61655-403-3

10 9 8 7 6 5 4 3 2 1
Printed in China

▷ No plants were harmed in the making of this comic. Countless zombies, however, definitely wer

MIKE RICHARDSON President and Publisher NEIL HANKERSON Executive Vice President TOM WEDDLE Chief Financial Officer RA
STRADLEY Vice President of Publishing MICHAEL MARTENS Vice President of Book Trade Sales ANITA NELSON Vice President of B
ness Affairs SCOTT ALLIE Editor in Chief MATT PARKINSON Vice President of Marketing DAVID SCROGGY Vice President of Proc
Development DALE LAFOUNTAIN Vice President of Information Technology DARLENE VOGEL Senior Director of Print, Design, and I
duction KEN LIZZI General Counsel DAVEY ESTRADA Editorial Director CHRIS WARNER Senior Books Editor DIANA SCHUTZ Execu
Editor CARY GRAZZINI Director of Print and Development LIA RIBACCHI Art Director CARA NIECE Director of Scheduling TIM WIES
Director of International Licensing MARK BERNARDI Director of Digital Publishing

DARKHORSE.COM / POPCAP.COM

HELLO?

AHHHHHHHH!

HEE-YAHHH!

URRK!

PUT!

OH! SORRY!

BUT WHY'D YOU ATTACK ME?

NO...MY... BAD. I'M SORRY... AND MY STOMACH IS REALLY SORRY.

OH, I THOUGHT YOU WERE ONE OF THESE.

ENEMIES!!

:ATE MUMMY

ALIEN NINJA

LASER CAVEMAN

SASQUATCH BALGRINA

YOU THOUGHT I WAS AN ALIEN NINJA?

NO. YES. I MEAN...THINGS SEEM *WEIRD* IN NEIGHBORVILLE TODAY.

I'M *NATE TIMELY*, BY THE WAY. ASPIRING *COWBOY ASTRONAUT*.

PATRICE BLAZING. PROFESSIONAL TREEHOUSE INVESTIGATOR.

AND WHAT DO YOU MEAN BY "*WEIRD*"...?

OH, JUST... THERE'S A PECULIAR *SMELL*. A TENSION IN THE AIR. I FEEL LIKE SOMETHING'S HAPPENING.

"SOME *EVIL* IS OUT THERE.

"SOME *MENACE* IS STALKING THE *STREETS*.

"IT'S *LURKING* IN THE *SHADOWS*.

BRAINS?

GOBBLE

MOMCH MUNCH

PLANT FOOD

"SPREADING A WAVE OF *SINISTER FOREBODING*."

PFAHHH!

PLANT FOOD

13

BRAINS!

BRAINS!

OKAY, DON'T MEAN TO COMPLAIN, BUT THAT'S, LIKE...AN OUTRAGEOUS NUMBER OF ZOMBIES.

BRAINS!

IT'S LIKE ANTS AT A PICNIC-- EXCEPT THEY DON'T WANT APPLE PIE OR SANDWICHES THEY WANT BRAINS AND WE HAVE BRAINS AND I DON'T LIKE THIS ANALOGY ANYMORE.

GRAB

AHHH!

AHHH!

GRUNGGG GRUNN GRUNGGG

HEY, DID YOU JUST HEAR A SORT OF "GRUNGGG GRUNN GRUNGGG" NOISE?

NO! I MOSTLY HEARD, LIKE...SO MANY ZOMBIES SAYING "BRAINS"...!

BRAINS.

BRAINS.

BRAINS.

BRAINS.

BRAINS.

BRAINS.

SEE? THAT'S A LITTLE MORE IMPORTANT THAN WHATEVER'S SAYING "GRUNGGG GRUNN GRUNGGG!"

BRAINS.

GRUNGGG

GRUNN

GRUNGGG

GRUNGGG

GRUNN

GRUNGGG

GRUNGGG

OKAY. MAYBE I WAS WRONG.

GRUNN

GRUNGGG

HOW MANY PLANTS ARE HERE, UNCLE DAVE?

GRAKKA GRAMMAL NOOB CHUM CHUM CHUM.

WHAT'S HE SAYING?

HE SAYS THERE ARE SIX HUNDRED AND FIFTY PLANTS HERE, ALL OF THEM BORN AND RAISED HERE IN HIS GARDEN LABORATORY, BUT...

"...HE'S BEEN INFUSING THE TOWN WITH THEM AS WELL...SO THERE ARE A LOT OF FREE-RANGE PLANTS OUT THERE IN NEIGHBORVILLE.

"AND SOME OF THEM ARE A LITTLE REBELLIOUS, SO THEY'VE BEEN GETTING OUT OF HIS HOTHOUSE GARDEN WHEN HE FORGETS TO CLOSE THE DOOR AND, ALSO...

NO ESCAPING! Please close door behind you after escaping.

"...HE SOMETIMES JUST LETS THEM *BORROW HIS CAR.*"

IS THAT SO WRONG?

OKAY, SO WE HAVE AN ARMY OF *INVADING* ZOMBIES. WHICH IS....*NOT* GOOD.

BUT WE *ALSO* HAVE AN ARMY OF *PLANTS!* THIS WILL WORK. *THIS* IS HOW WE'LL SAVE NEIGHBORVILLE.

WE'LL FIGHT THEM ON THE *SIDEWALKS!* ON THE *ROOFTOPS!* ON THE *STREETS!* IN THE *BACKYARDS!*

NOW WHO'S *WITH ME?!*

ME.

SERIOUSLY?

NO ONE ELSE?

INVADING ARMY?

FIGHT FOR JUSTICE?

ANTI CATNIP

ANTI-CATNET

ANTIPASTO!

ANYONE?

HURRAH!

24

OKAY! YOU GUYS ARE IN?! GREAT!

UMM. YIKES! WHOA. HEY.

P-THOOP

P-THOOP

P-THOOP

TONE DOWN THE CELEBRATION A BIT, WOULD YOU?

P-THOOP

B-DONK

THE WALL-NUTS AND THE TALL-NUTS STAND WITH YOU.

B-DONK

THEY DO? THAT'S GREAT!

HIGH-FIVE, GUYS!

YEAH. NOT GONNA WORK, NATE.

BROGGLE SIDEWALK BRAGG ZOMBIE-STINKER GIBBLY LEMONADE FROMPING.

DAVE SAYS THAT MOST OF THESE PLANTS HAVEN'T ENCOUNTERED THE ZOMBIES...YET.

SO, IF WE WANT TO RECRUIT THEM, WE HAVE TO GO OUT INTO THE TOWN. TALK TO THE PLANTS THAT ARE ALREADY FIGHTING THE WAR...

ALSO, HE WANTS SOME LEMONADE.

YEAH. LEMONADE WOULD BE GOOD.

SOON...

BRAINS.

HOW ARE THINGS GOING SO FAR, NATE?

GREAT! HFF! HFF! SWELL! NO PROBLEMS ON THIS END! HEY... HFF! HFF! CAN I CALL YOU BACK IN A BIT?

AND...

BRAINS.

BRAINS.

SO, YOU SEEING ANY ZOMBIES?

OH, A COUPLE. JUST HERE AND THERE.

NOPE. NOTHING REALLY GOING ON OVER HERE. NOTHING TO BE CONCERNED ABOUT.

ARE YOU JUST SAYING THAT SO I DON'T WORRY?

HA! ME? NO WAY!

BRAINS.

BRAINS.

BRAINS.

IT'S JUST THAT THINGS ARE LOOKING SO GREAT, AND I'M REALLY ENJOYING MY RIDE!

BRAINS.

The Daily Dave — CATS PAISED AT BORDER!

THINGS NOT LOOKING GOOD FOR NATE.

IS CEREBRAL SPINAL FLUID THE NEXT SUGAR SUBSTITUTE?

NATE, YOU'RE BEING SWARMED BY ZOMBIES, AREN'T YOU?

NO! WELL HARDLY. I MEAN, KIND OF. ACTUALLY, YEAH...A LOT.

ARE THERE ANY PLANTS HELPING YOU? SEEN ANY?

NOT SO FAR. HFF! HFF! BUT I'M HOPING THAT--

GLOMPFF

GRRK?

YES!

NATE, WHAT JUST HAPPENED?

A CACTUS WALL! THE ZOMBIES ARE STUCK! OOOH. REALLY LOOKS LIKE IT WOULD HURT.

BUT... HOW ARE YOU DOING?

EVERYTHING'S GOOD. ONLY AN OCCASIONAL ZOMBIE.

AND I'M JUST NOW STARTING TO SEE SOME OF UNCLE DAVE'S PLANTS.

HARDWA

I'LL NEED TO FIND THE MAIN GROUP OF THEM-- AND THEN WE CAN MOBILIZE THEM INTO AN ARMY.

UNTIL THEN, I JUST HOPE...

...THAT I DON'T RUN INTO ANYTHING...

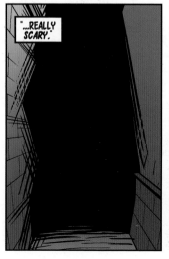

"...REALLY SCARY."

BRAINS!

BRAINS!

THIS IS HOW NEIGHBORVILLE IS SUPPOSED TO LOOK.

THIS IS HOW IT CURRENTLY LOOKS.

THIS IS HOW NATE TIMELY IS SUPPOSED TO LOOK.

THIS IS HOW HE CURRENTLY LOOKS.

GAHHHH!

BRAINS!

BRAINS!

BRAINS!

BRAINS!

LITTLE *HELP* HERE, GUYS!

!!!

BRAINS!

BRAINS!

THOOT

THOOT

THOOT

BRAINS?

BRAINS?

SPAKK

SPAKK

SPAKK

BRAINS?

BRAINS?

YES!

PATRICE? ARE YOU *THERE?* THIS IS *NATE.*

I'VE FOUND SOME OF THOSE PLANTS THAT *CRAZY...UHH.* YOUR *UNCLE* DAVE SET LOOSE IN TOWN.

"I'VE CONVINCED THEM TO *HELP,* BUT THE ZOMBIES ARE *EVERYWHERE!*"

BRAINS?

QUACK! QUACK! QUACK!*

*TRANSLATION: AHHHHH!

SPLITT

SPLITT

SPLITT

SPLITT

SPLITT

SPLITT

"IT'S A *WAR ZONE* OUT HERE, AND THE PLANTS ARE GETTING *EXHAUSTED.*"

I'VE ONLY MANAGED TO FIND *FIVE* SUNFLOWERS. THEY'RE PROVIDING SOME ENERGY FOR THE PLANTS...

...BUT THEY CAN'T KEEP IT UP MUCH LONGER.

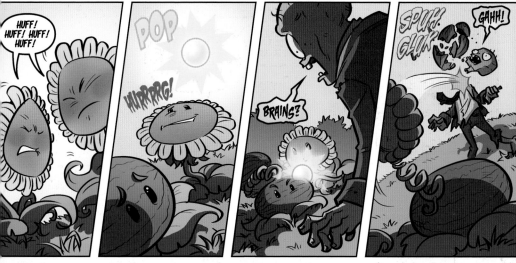

HUFF! HUFF! HUFF! HUFF!

POP

HURRRRG!

BRAINS?

SPUH. GLUK.

GAHH!

DID YOU... HFF! HFF!...FIND THAT GROUP OF SUNFLOWERS YOU WERE LOOKING FOR?

JOHN'S PIZZA. WHAT WOULD YOU LIKE ON YOUR PIZZA, SIR?

BRAINS...

BRAINS...

PATRICE? WHY AREN'T YOU *ANSWERING*?

PATRICE?

ARE YOU THERE?

HA! SEE YOU LATER, YETI-GATOR!

ZWOOOP!

THANKS! I THOUGHT I WAS A--

--GONER.

BRAINS.

BRAINS.

BRAINS.

OKAY. TIME FOR PLAN C.

AND "C" STANDS FOR CHAOS.

STREEEETCH

STREEEETCH

STREEEETCH

STREEETCH

STREEETCH

BUNGEE SLAM!!!

OH. THAT WAS AWESOME.

I'M AWESOME.

EVERYTHING'S AWESOME.

EH?

TAP TAP TAP

AWESOME!

Calling...

BEEP BOOP BEEP

OKAY, OKAY! GOTTA THINK THIS THROUGH. THERE *HAS* TO BE SOME WAY OUT OF THIS.

AHHH! GOT IT!

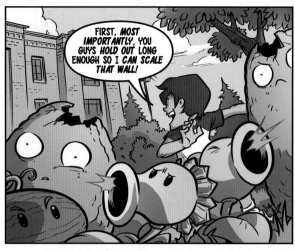

FIRST, *MOST IMPORTANTLY,* YOU GUYS HOLD OUT LONG ENOUGH SO I CAN SCALE *THAT WALL!*

"THEN I'LL SWING FROM ROOFTOP TO ROOFTOP USING A *GRAPPLING HOOK!* IT'LL BE *GREAT!*"

TA-DAH!

BRAINS? BRAINS? BRAINS?

"I'LL PROBABLY HAVE TO DO SOME SWORD FIGHTING, BUT THAT'S OKAY."

BRAINS?

EN GARDE, ROTTED ONE!

MEANWHILE, YOU *GUYS* KEEP UP THE ONGOING FIRE.

AND YOU GUYS SLOW THEM UP SO THESE GUYS CAN FLATTEN THEM.

YOU CHOMPER PLANTS JUST, UM, *TOTALLY CHOMP* ON ZOMBIES!

THEN *I* COME BACK WITH *PATRICE* AND THE *SUNFLOWERS,* AND HOPEFULLY THE *ARMY* AND THE *NAVY* AND SOME *COOKIES.*

MAN...I COULD *REALLY* USE SOME COOKIES.

I THINK THAT'S IT. I'VE DONE IT. THIS PLAN'S GOING TO WORK.

I'M THE PRESIDENT OF PERFECT PLANNING. I'M THE KING OF KICK BUTT. I'M TOTALLY THE FIVE-STAR GENERAL OF ZOMBIE DEVASTATION.

KRAKKA-KOOOOM

HUH?

THMMP

STOMP

STOMP

WHA--? UH-OH.

STOMP
STOMP

OH, DANG. I'M ABOUT TO BECOME THE PRINCE OF GETTING POUNDED.

HUH?

SQUASH!

SQUASH!

SQUASH!

SQUASH!

YES!

HA! YOU GUYS MADE IT!

I KNEW YOU WOULDN'T LET ME DOWN! NEVER WORRIED FOR A SECOND! I WASN'T EVEN NERVOUS! NOT A BIT!

YOU DIDN'T HEAR ME SCREAMING, DID YOU?

NO? GOOD.

BUT, WHERE DID THOSE GARGANTUAR ZOMBIES COME FROM? SOMEWHERE NEAR THE CENTER OF TOWN?

LOOKS LIKE WE CAN FOLLOW THE TRAIL.

SOON. FIVE BLOCKS LATER...

!

!

!

≈GASP!≈

!

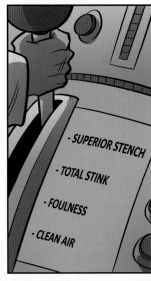

- SUPERIOR STENCH

- TOTAL STINK

- FOULNESS

- CLEAN AIR

WHO IS THAT? SOME SORT OF... ZOMBOSS?

BUT...WHAT'S THAT MACHINE GONNA DO?

PATRICE. I THINK I FOUND THE LEADER OF THE ZOMBIES.

YOU MEAN THE SUPER-UGLY ONE NEXT TO THE MACHINE?

WELL, ALL OF THE ZOMBIES ARE SUPER UGLY--BUT, YES, THE ONE NEXT TO THE MACHINE.

HOW DID YOU KNOW? WHERE ARE YOU?

BEHIND YOU. LOOK UP. AND WAVE.

HUH?

HEY, NATE.

HI, PATRICE.

C'MON! MY UNCLE DAVE ALWAYS KNOWS WHAT TO DO!

YOU GUYS, CLIMB ABOARD!

YEAH! PILE ON, AND HANG ON!

OUCH! WHOSE ROOTS ARE THESE?

SOMEBODY'S LEAVES ARE IN MY FACE!

ZOMBIES! DO WE GO AROUND THEM?

ARE YOU KIDDING? WE'RE LIKE BATTLESHIPS!

BATTLESHIPS DON'T HAVE TO GO AROUND ANYTHING.

...THE HEADLIGHTS FROM NINE MOTORCYCLES, A COMPLETE SET OF THE ADVENTURES OF CAPTAIN CATERPILLAR...

"...AND AT LEAST FIFTY-FIVE PACKAGES OF DECENT SHOE INSERTS..."

...THEN HE CAN MAKE A LIFE-SIZE T. REX THAT BREATHES FIRE!

EHHH?

WHAT'S THAT GOT TO DO WITH THE GIANT CLOUD?

NOTHING. BUT IT WOULD BE REALLY NEAT!

BRAINS!

BRAINS!

BRAINS!

BRAINS!

BRAINS!

UNNN...

BRAINS?

WHY ARE YOU STOPPING?

SCREECH

RED LIGHT! WE HAVE TO STOP AT A RED LIGHT!

NATE, THE ZOMBIES AREN'T GOING TO STOP AT A RED LIGHT... SO WE DON'T EITHER!

ZOOOM

BUT...

DID THEY... DID THEY ACTUALLY STOP?

YEAH. THEY DID. BECAUSE RUNNING A RED LIGHT IS *ILLEGAL*, PATRICE.

OKAY, I'M *SORRY!* BUT AT LEAST THIS WILL GIVE US TIME TO SET UP A DEFENSE.

RIGHT. WE CAN'T SEEM TO GET AWAY FROM THESE GUYS. WE'RE CLEARLY GOING TO HAVE TO *FIGHT* OUR WAY TO THE MANSION--AND THE *WIND MACHINE.*

TIME TO GET *SERIOUS*, THEN. I BROUGHT... *STICKERS!*

STICKERS? WHAT ARE YOU DOING?

IT'S THE STICKERS MY TEACHER HANDS OUT WHEN WE DO A GOOD JOB! IT SHOULD ENCOURAGE THE PLANTS!

CERTIFIED GOOD JOB!

LOOK OUT BEL-*UMPFFF!*

ACK!

!

!

YOU KNOW, MAYBE STOPPING TO FIGHT *WASN'T* THE SMARTEST THING TO DO.

I KNOW. WE'RE BEING *OVERWHELMED* HERE.

THE SUNFLOWERS ARE *EXHAUSTED.*

IT'S TOO *DARK.* THERE'S NO *SUN ENERGY* TO BE HAD.

AND THERE'S *WAY* TOO MANY *ZOMBIES.*

NATE, THIS LOOKS *BAD.*

UMMM... PANCAKES?

THAT'S IT? I THOUGHT HE WAS GOING TO GIVE US A RIDE TO THE MANSION OR SOMETHING.

YOBBLE?

OH...YEAH. YOU KNOW, THAT WOULD BE FOR THE BEST!

UNCLE DAVE LOVES TO USE THE CAR, BECAUSE EVERY TIME HE DOES, IT COOKS PANCAKES!

UH. WHAT?

SEE? IT HAS A GRILL AND A PANCAKE BATTER DISPENSER BUILT INTO THE ENGINE!

THAT'S... AMAZING. SERIOUSLY THOUGH, KINDA FIGHTING SOME ZOMBIES HERE!

OH, YEAH!

RIGHT! EVERYBODY GET IN!

I'M STARTING TO THINK MAYBE THEIR WHOLE FAMILY IS, YOU KNOW, A LITTLE SHORT IN THE BRAINS.

BRAINS?

BRAINS?

ROOOOARRRR!

BRAINS?

HUH? BUT IF CRAZY DAVE IS OUT *THERE*, THEN....WHO'S *DRIVING?*

THIS *SQUASH* IS DRIVING. UNCLE DAVE NEEDED TO GO OFF IN SEARCH OF *TELEPATHIC SQUIRRELS* FOR A LITTLE SIDE PROJECT HE'S WORKING ON.

NOTHING TO WORRY ABOUT!

I'M NOT WORRIED ABOUT *TELEPATHIC SQUIRRELS!* I'M WORRIED ABOUT A *PLANT DRIVING THE CAR!*

SHOULDN'T BE A PROBLEM. MY UNCLE SAID HE'S A GOOD DRIVER.

OH. WELL. OKAY.

ZOOOOOOM

ACTUALLY, YOU KNOW WHAT? I AM A LITTLE WORRIED ABOUT *TELEPATHIC SQUIRRELS.*

SOON...

HERE WE ARE.

GREAT. I SEE THE WIND MACHINE AT THE TOP, THERE.

BUT, WOW, THIS PLACE LOOKS SPOOKY.

LOOKS CAN BE DECEIVING. I KNOW IT LOOKS LIKE A HAUNTED MANSION, BUT IT'S A GREAT HOUSE!

THERE'S NO GHOSTS OR DEMONS OR ZOMBIES OR WEREWOLVES OR ANYTHING LIKE THAT.

WAIT...DID I SAY NO ZOMBIES?

YOU DID.

OH, WELL... MY BAD. THERE ARE A LOT OF ZOMBIES.

BRAINS?

THIS ISN'T A BAD HOUSE, REALLY. I *LIKE* WHAT YOU'VE DONE WITH THE PLACE. WELL, YOU KNOW--

--EXCEPT FOR ALL THE ZOMBIES!

BRAINS?

BRAINS?

THE KITCHEN'S NICE.

BRAINS?

BRAINS?

KEEP SHOOTING, GUYS!

WE HAVE TO MAKE IT TO THE *WIND MACHINE!* TWO MORE STORIES TO GO!

TWO MORE STORIES? DO THESE STORIES HAVE ANY ZOMBIES IN THEM? I *DON'T* LIKE ZOMBIE STORIES ANYMORE!

SPAKK!

SPAKK!

B-TOOP!

B-TOOP!

B-TOOP!

SPAKK!

SPAKK!

THERE! THE SWITCH FOR THE WIND MACHINE!

TURN IT ON!

HEY! WHO--?

WHOA! UMM, PATRICE? THIS WOULDN'T HAPPEN TO BE SOME PARTICULARLY UGLY COUSIN OF YOURS, WOULD IT?

SQUASH! GET HIM!

KLUMPF

WHOOSH

WHAPPP!

WARRGG!

P-TOO! P-TOO!

SWATTT!

THE PEASHOOTERS AREN'T *HURTING* HIM!

AND THE SQUASH CAN'T *GET* TO HIM!

SQUASH! ALL OF YOU! POUND DOWN *RIGHT HERE!*

HUH? NATE? WHY WOULD THEY--?

CRASHHH!!

WARRRG!

BRAINS?

OH.

DOWNTOWN NEIGHBORVILLE...

FIND THAT ZOMBOSS!

LET'S WIN THIS WAR!

BRAINS!

BRAINS!

GARRR!

SPLATCH

GUH?

BRAINS?

SQUASH

OOOH.

WE'RE *NOT* BACKING *DOWN!* CONCENTRATE FIRE ON THE *GARGANTUARS!*

SPLUTCH

P-THOOP?

THOONT

THOONT

TRY TO BRING THEM *DOWN!*

WHHH-WHOOSH

WHOOOSHHH

P-TOO P-TOO

PROTECT THE *SUNFLOWERS* FROM THE *INCOMING* FIRE!

THAPPT

THAPPT

THAPPT

GRRR-ARRR! BRAINS!

I NEED MORE CHERRY BOMBS!

HA HA HAAA! YES! YES!

HEY! MY BIKE! THAT'S RUDE!

NATE! THE PLANTS ARE GETTING *BEATEN!*

YEAH, THERE'S MORE ZOMBIES THAN I THOUGHT! AND THAT ZOMBOSS IS *ORGANIZING* THEM! HE'S TOO *SMART* FOR US!

WE NEED SOMEONE WITH *BRAINS* ON *OUR* SIDE.

74

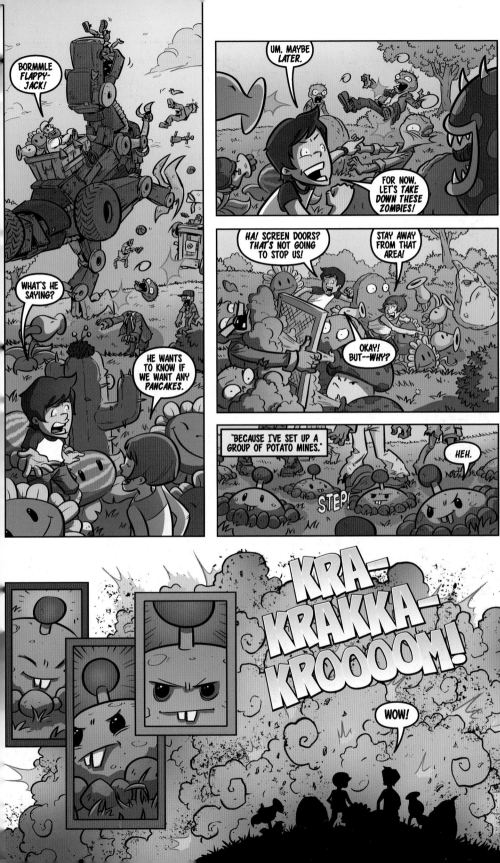

Paul Tobin

Ron Chan

Matthew J. Rainwater

CREATOR BIOS

PAUL TOBIN is a critically acclaimed bald guy who had his first encounter with zombies when he watched the 1973 film *Children Shouldn't Play with Dead Things* on late-night television during one of the first times his parents ever left him alone. They returned to find him cowering in the kitchen with a knife. Paul eventually recovered enough mental stability to go on to write hundreds of comics for Marvel, DC, Dark Horse, and many others, including creator-owned titles such as *Colder* and *Bandette*, as well as *Prepare to Die!*—his debut novel. Paul's favorite zombie-fighting plants are the Cattail, the Snow Pea, and the Spikerock.

RON CHAN was born and raised in Portland, Oregon, and works as a freelance cartoonist, storyboard artist, and illustrator. He graduated from the Savannah College of Art and Design in 2005, and is now a member of the Portland-based art collective Periscope Studio. His comic-book work has been published by Dark Horse, Marvel, Image, Virgin, and Viper Comics. Storyboarding work of his includes boards for 3-D animation, gaming, internal development, user-experience design, and advertising for clients such as Microsoft, Dell, Amazon Kindle, Nike, Konami, and Sega. His first *Plants vs. Zombies* play-through was in 2009 on Steam for PC, and he prefers a Starfruit and Garlic-based defense strategy.

MATTHEW J. RAINWATER is a freelance cartoonist recently transplanted from the warm, humid swamps of Louisiana to the cool, damp forests of Portland, Oregon. A graduate of the Savannah College of Art and Design, Matt has worked on freelance illustration for advertising firms, web design, and independent video games. On top of this, he also self-publishes several comic books, including *Garage Raja* and *Trailer Park Warlock*, both of which can be found at GarageRaja.com. Matt finally beat *Plants vs. Zombies* in 2013 on his PC, and his zombie-smashing strategies tend toward Kernel-pults and Peashooters with a strong Squash and Wall-nut defensive line.

DARK HORSE VIDEO GAME INSPIRED TITLES

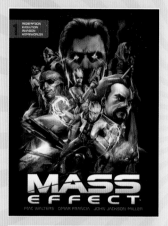

MASS EFFECT

The series that revolutionized video game comics gets a deluxe treatment. Created in close collaboration with the writers of the games, including *Mass Effect 2* and *3* lead writer Mac Walters, the *Mass Effect* comics are tightly integrated and essential chapters of gaming's most acclaimed science fiction epic.

Mass Effect Library Edition
ISBN 978-1-61655-111-7

DRAGON AGE

Fans around the world have recognized the *Dragon Age* comics to be an integral addition to BioWare's video-game saga. Now, series writer David Gaider pits King Alistair and his noble companions Varric and Isabela against their most nefarious foe—the twisted blood mage Aurelian Titus!

Dragon Age Volume 1: The Silent Grove
ISBN 978-1-59582-916-0

Dragon Age Volume 2: Those Who Speak
ISBN 978-1-61655-053-0

Dragon Age Volume 3: Until We Sleep
ISBN 978-1-61655-219-0

ALICE: MADNESS RETURNS

Take a journey through the wonderland of legendary game designer American McGee's imagination for an unprecedented look at the creation of this magnificent and disturbing world. *The Art of Alice* offers an intimate look into the stunning and terrifying artwork behind this blockbuster reinterpretation of Lewis Carroll's enduring masterpiece!

The Art of Alice: Madness Returns
ISBN 978-1-59582-697-8

MORE DARK HORSE ALL-AGES TITLES

CHIMICHANGA

When Wrinkle's Traveling Circus's adorable little bearded girl trades a lock of her magic beard hair for a witch's strange egg, she stumbles upon what could be the saving grace for her ailing freak show: the savory-named beast Chimichanga!

Chimichanga
ISBN 978-1-59582-755-5

FLUFFY

Fluffy is a young rabbit with a human daddy named Michael. One day Michael decides to take Fluffy away for an impromptu trip to visit relatives in Sicily. Neither bunny nor man is truly prepared for the worldly excitement of a suspected kidnapping in Sicily, and both will be forever changed by the experience.

Fluffy
ISBN 978-1-59307-972-7

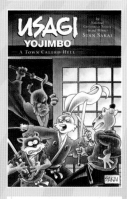

USAGI YOJIMBO

The rabbit *ronin* Usagi's wanderings find him caught between competing gang lords fighting for control of a town called Hell, confronting a *nukekubi*—a flying cannibal head—and crossing paths with the demon Jei!

Usagi Yojimbo Volume 25: Fox Hunt
ISBN 978-1-59582-726-5

Usagi Yojimbo Volume 26: Traitors of the Earth
ISBN 978-1-59582-910-8

Usagi Yojimbo Volume 27: A Town Called Hell
ISBN 978-1-59582-970-2

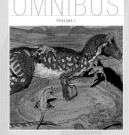

AGE OF REPTILES

When Ricardo Delgado first set his sights on creating comics, he crafted an epic tale about the most unlikely cast of characters: dinosaurs. Since that first Eisner-winning foray into the world of sequential art, he has returned to his critically acclaimed *Age of Reptiles* again and again, each time crafting a captivating saga about his saurian subjects.

Age of Reptiles Omnibus
ISBN 978-1-59582-683-1